Verbal Reasoning

Rapid Tests 1

Siân Goodspeed

Schofield&Sims

Introduction

This book gives you practice in answering verbal reasoning questions quickly.

The questions are like the questions on the 11+ and other school selection tests. You must find the correct answers.

School selection tests are usually timed, so you need to get used to working quickly. Each test has a target time for you to work towards. Ask an adult to time you.

What you need

- A pencil
- An eraser
- A clock, watch or stopwatch
- A sheet of rough paper
- An adult to time you and to mark the test for you

What to do

- Turn to **Section 1 Test 1** on page 4. Look at the grey box at the top of the page labelled **Target time**. This tells you how long the test should take.
- The adult helping you will tell you when to begin.
- Find this arrow ↓ near the top of the first page. Start each test here.
- Find this square ■. The instructions for the first set of questions are beside it. Read them carefully.
- Look below the instructions. Read the **Example**. Work out why the answer given is correct.
- Use a similar method to answer question 1. Show your answer in the way that the answer is shown in the example. For instance, you might need to write your answer on the line or underline the correct answer.
- Try to answer every question. If you do get stuck on a question, leave it and go on to the next one. Work quickly and try your best.
- Each test is one page long. When you reach the end, stop and tell the adult that you have finished.
- The adult will mark your test. Then the adult will fill in the **Score**, **Time taken** and **Target met?** boxes at the end of the test.
- Turn to the **Progress chart** on page 40. Write your score in the box and colour in the graph to show how many questions you got right.
- Did you get some questions wrong? You should always have another go at them before you look at the answers. Then ask the adult to check your work and help you if you are still not sure.
- Later, you will do some more of these tests. You will soon learn to work through them more quickly. The adult who is helping you will tell you what to do next.

Published by ***Schofield & Sims Ltd,***
7 Mariner Court, Wakefield, West Yorkshire WF4 3FL, UK
Telephone 01484 607080
www.schofieldandsims.co.uk

First published in 2014
This edition copyright © Schofield & Sims Ltd, 2018
Second impression 2019

Author: ***Siân Goodspeed****. Siân Goodspeed has asserted her moral right under the Copyright, Designs and Patents Act, 1988, to be identified as the author of this work.*

British Library Cataloguing in Publication Data. *A catalogue record for this book is available from the British Library.*

Commissioned by ***Carolyn Richardson Publishing Services*** *(www.publiserve.co.uk)*

Design by ***Oxford Designers & Illustrators***
Front cover design by ***Ledgard Jepson Ltd***
Printed in the UK by ***Page Bros (Norwich) Ltd***
ISBN 978 07217 1450 9

Contents

A **pull-out answers section** (pages A1 to A8) appears in the centre of this book, between pages 20 and 21. It also gives simple guidance on how best to use this book. Remove this section before the child begins working through the tests.

Section 1 Test 1

Target time: **12 minutes**

Underline the two words, **one** from each group, that mean almost the **same**.

Example (hot, cool, heat) (sky, day, cold)

1. (quick, run, wait) (walk, fast, sit)
2. (sound, noisy, radio) (bang, shout, loud)
3. (jumper, sneeze, cold) (sunny, chilly, scarf)

Choose the word in brackets that will complete the sentence in the best way. Underline the answer.

Example **Cat** is to **kitten** as **dog** is to (paw, puppy, animal).

4. **Little** is to **mouse** as **enormous** is to (rat, hippopotamus, hamster).
5. **Drive** is to **car** as **ride** is to (person, bike, lorry).
6. **Father** is to **man** as **mother** is to (sister, woman, kind).

Underline the two words, **one** from each group, that are most **opposite** in meaning.

Example (large, down, in) (tiny, tree, hat)

7. (big, up, round) (small, horse, hill)
8. (day, early, sun) (sleep, night, bed)
9. (house, in, door) (shop, out, about)

Underline the word that goes best with the three words in brackets.

Example (bonnet, cap, beanie) hat, coat, shoes

10. (car, van, lorry) boat, train, truck
11. (star, triangle, square) circle, clown, tree
12. (high, above, raised) up, down, below

Score:		Time taken:		Target met?	

Target time: **12 minutes**

1–3. For each of the words below, choose the correct group. Write its letter on the line.

A = animal **I** = insect

deer ____________ tiger ____________

beetle ____________ bee ____________

rabbit ____________ fly ____________

In each group, three words go together and one is the odd one out. Underline the word that does **not** go with the other three.

Example one two <u>out</u> six

4. cat dog sun mouse

5. blue purple yellow door

6. duck monkey swan seagull

Underline the two words, **one** from each group, that are most **opposite** in meaning.

Example (<u>big</u>, up, round) (<u>small</u>, elephant, house)

7. (roof, man, high) (mat, garden, low)

8. (top, shoe, stairs) (table, bottom, rest)

9. (press, open, play) (shut, cry, put)

Two words in each sentence must change places so that the sentence makes sense. Underline the two words.

Example Where do you <u>to</u> <u>go</u> school? (Where do you go to school?)

10. How are old you?

11. Is what your name?

12. Where do live you?

Score:		**Time taken:**		**Target met?**	

Section 1 Test 3

Target time: **12 minutes**

Underline the pair of words that mean almost the **same**.

Example (hot, cool) (freezing, sunny) (<u>cool, cold</u>)

1. (box, door) (shut, close) (window, lid)
2. (lose, look) (angry, cross) (frown, blink)
3. (dream, better) (sleep, food) (sick, ill)

Choose the word in brackets that will complete the sentence in the best way. Underline the answer.

Example **Cat** is to **kitten** as **dog** is to (paw, <u>puppy</u>, animal).

4. **Television** is to **watch** as **book** is to (read, eat, play).
5. **Funny** is to **laugh** as **sad** is to (smile, cry, blue).
6. **Winter** is to **snowy** as **summer** is to (sunny, icy, holiday).

7–9. For each of the words below, choose the correct group. Write its letter on the line.

F = fruit **V** = vegetable

apple ____________ parsnip ____________

orange ____________ potato ____________

carrot ____________ cabbage ____________

In each group, three words go together and one is the odd one out. Underline the word that does **not** go with the other three.

Example one two <u>out</u> six

10. library sand bucket spade
11. paw foot tail hoof
12. small tiny large little

Score:		**Time taken:**		**Target met?**	

Target time: **12 minutes**

Find the missing letters in each word. Choose from the letters given below. You may only use each letter once. Write the missing letter on the line.

a h o m b e

Example h _a_ t

1. __ in
2. __ ip
3. __ gg

In each of the sentences below, the word in capitals has three letters missing. Those three letters spell a word. Write the three-letter word in the gap.

Example She left the door O _P_ _E_ _N_. (OPEN)

4. The MON __ __ __ ate a banana.
5. Will you P __ __ __ with me?
6. I will S __ __ __ you how it works.

If these words were listed in alphabetical order, which word would come **first**? Write the answer on the line.

Example dog cat vet sit cow _cat_

7. man fat rib cap ____________
8. dip mop ant boy ____________
9. pan zoo you toe ____________

Find the missing letter that completes **both** words. Write the letter on the line. Choose your answer from these letters:

l t h

Example tap (_e_) at (tape and eat)

10. wis (__) ope
11. boo (__) ent
12. rea (__) ick

Score:		Time taken:		Target met?	

Section 1 Test 5

Target time: **12 minutes**

In each of the sentences below, the word in capitals has three letters missing. Those three letters spell a word. Write the three-letter word in the gap.

Example She left the door O _P_ _E_ _N_. (OPEN)

1. I paid the B ___ ___ ___.
2. He lit the fire with a ___ ___ ___ CH.
3. The little boy fell D ___ ___ ___.

Find the **three-letter word** hidden in each longer word. You will not need to change the letter order. Underline the word and write it on the line.

Example la<u>the</u> the

4. ripple ____________
5. thrill ____________
6. dear ____________

Underline the **two** words that contain all the same letters.

Example two <u>now</u> was <u>won</u> you

7. tea get ear let are
8. who yaw tow way tag
9. wow woe how eye who

Underline the two words, **one** from each group, that together make one new word. The word from the first group comes first.

Example (<u>foot</u>, head, face) (shoe, <u>ball</u>, mask) (football)

10. (circle, round, oval) (under, about, in)
11. (gold, ice, water) (ring, pot, fish)
12. (cow, milk, dairy) (shake, glass, farm)

Score:		Time taken:		Target met?	

Target time: **12 minutes**

Change the first word into the last word. Only change **one** letter at a time. You must make a new word in the middle. Write the new word on the line.

Example MAN [PAN] PIN

1. TOP [________] NIP
2. PAT [________] POP
3. SIT [________] SAG

In each of the sentences below, the word in capitals has three letters missing. Those three letters spell a word. Write the three-letter word in the gap.

Example She left the door O P E N. (OPEN)

4. I did not want to S _ _ _ playing on the swings.
5. The little girl had fun at the BIRTH _ _ _ party.
6. We played FOOTB _ _ _ together.

Underline the two words, **one** from each group, that together make one new word. The word from the first group comes first.

Example (foot, head, face) (shoe, ball, mask) (football)

7. (house, pan, cook) (cake, heat, cookie)
8. (bread, butter, cheese) (run, fly, jump)
9. (group, class, learn) (house, room, teach)

If these words were listed in alphabetical order, which word would come **last**? Write the answer on the line.

Example dog cat vet sit cow vet

10. sky try rot lop ________
11. go now the sip ________
12. mat hip dot fan ________

Score:		**Time taken:**		**Target met?**	

Section 1 Test 7

Target time: **12 minutes**

Find the next number in the sequence. Write it on the line.

Example 14 15 16 17 18 ___19___ (+1 each time)

1. 6 7 8 9 10 ______
2. 3 4 5 6 7 ______
3. 13 14 15 16 17 ______

Use the information given to answer the sum. Write your answer as a **letter**.

Example A = 1 B = 2 C = 3 D = 5 **A + B =** ___C___ (1 + 2 = 3)

4. A = 5 B = 7 C = 13 D = 12 **A + B =** ______
5. A = 17 B = 9 C = 14 D = 8 **D + B =** ______
6. A = 5 B = 11 C = 16 D = 12 **B + A =** ______

Work out the missing number. Write it on the line.

Example 3 [5] 2 4 [6] 2 5 [___8___] 3
(a + b = ?, where a is the number on the left and b is the number on the right)

7. 14 [15] 1 13 [15] 2 12 [______] 3
8. 4 [3] 1 5 [4] 1 6 [______] 1
9. 3 [10] 7 4 [10] 6 1 [______] 9

Find the missing number in each equation. Write it on the line.

Example 1 + 3 = 2 + ___2___ (1 + 3 = 4 and so does 2 + 2)

10. 4 − 1 = 5 − ______
11. 5 + 1 = 3 + ______
12. 10 − 7 = 2 + ______

Score:		**Time taken:**		**Target met?**	

Target time: **12 minutes**

Work out the missing number. Write it on the line.

Example 3 [5] 2 4 [6] 2 5 [8] 3
(a + b = ?, where a is the number on the left and b is the number on the right)

1. 7 [9] 2 8 [12] 4 5 [______] 10
2. 3 [16] 13 14 [26] 12 15 [______] 1
3. 15 [2] 13 16 [12] 4 7 [______] 2

Find the missing number in each equation. Write it on the line.

Example 1 + 3 = 2 + 2 (1 + 3 = 4 and so does 2 + 2)

4. 16 + 3 = 9 + ______
5. 40 − 30 = 1 + ______
6. 2 + 3 = 5 + ______

Find the next number in the sequence. Write it on the line.

Example 14 15 16 17 18 19 (+1 each time)

7. 27 28 29 30 31 ______
8. 47 46 45 44 43 ______
9. 3 5 7 9 11 ______

Use the information given to answer the sum. Write your answer as a **letter**.

Example A = 1 B = 2 C = 3 D = 5 **A + B =** C (1 + 2 = 3)

10. A = 3 B = 6 C = 6 D = 9 **A + C =** ______
11. A = 11 B = 4 C = 6 D = 7 **D + B =** ______
12. A = 9 B = 15 C = 8 D = 6 **B − D =** ______

Score:		**Time taken:**		**Target met?**	

Section 1 Test 9

Target time: **15 minutes**

Find the next letter in the sequence. Use the alphabet to help you. Write the letter on the line.

A B C D E F G H I J K L M N O P Q R S T U V W X Y Z

Example A B C D E F (+1 each time)

1. L M N O P ______
2. T S R Q P ______
3. D G D G D ______

Find the letter that completes each sentence. Use the alphabet to help you. Write the letter on the line.

A B C D E F G H I J K L M N O P Q R S T U V W X Y Z

Example **A** is to **B** as **D** is to E. (+1 each time)

4. **L** is to **K** as **E** is to ______ .
5. **P** is to **S** as **H** is to ______ .
6. **N** is to **P** as **B** is to ______ .

Make a new word. Change the third pair of words in the same way as the other pairs. Write the new word on the line.

Example (mat, at) (fit, it) (son, on) (take away the first letter of the first word)

7. (pop, pope) (mop, mope) (hop, ______________)
8. (mane, man) (vane, van) (pane, ______________)
9. (hat, hate) (rat, rate) (mat, ______________)

Match the number codes to the words. Use this to help you work out the answers to the questions. Write your answers on the lines.

TOE ONE TAN 153 413 465

10. What is the code for **TAN**? ______________
11. What is the code for **TOE**? ______________
12. What does the code **153** mean? ______________

Score:		**Time taken:**		**Target met?**	

Target time: **15 minutes**

Find the code. Use the alphabet to help you. Write the code on the line.

A B C D E F G H I J K L M N O P Q R S T U V W X Y Z

Example If the code for **TOP** is **UPQ**, what is the code for **TIP**? UJQ (+1 each time)

1. If the code for **TOP** is **UPQ**, what is the code for **POT**? ____________
2. If the code for **HIT** is **IJU**, what is the code for **END**? ____________
3. If the code for **NOT** is **OPU**, what is the code for **BOY**? ____________

Match the number codes to the words. Use this to help you work out the answers to the questions. Write your answers on the lines.

USE SET SUN 174 135 713

4. What is the code for **SET**? ____________
5. What is the code for **SUN**? ____________
6. What does the code **713** mean? ____________

The word in square brackets has been made by some of the letters from the two outside words. Make a new word in the middle of the second group of words in the same way. Write the new word on the line.

Example (toe [tap] rap) (low [lit] sit)

7. (bus [bat] cat) (sun [____________] mat)
8. (ran [ant] tip) (lit [____________] sap)
9. (toe [tap] lap) (bat [____________] run)

Find the next letter in the sequence. Use the alphabet to help you. Write the letter on the line.

A B C D E F G H I J K L M N O P Q R S T U V W X Y Z

Example A B C D E F (+1 each time)

10. R S R S R ____
11. V W V W V ____
12. T U V W X ____

Score:		**Time taken:**		**Target met?**	

Section 1 Test 11

Target time: **15 minutes**

Read the following information. Work out the answers. Write your answers on the lines.

1. James is having a race with 2 of his friends. James does not win the race but he does not come last either. In what place does James finish the race? ____________________

2. Three people are standing in a line. Shameet is first in the line. Sally is second in the line. Sally is standing in front of Greg. Where is Greg in the line? ____________________

3. Jack has 11 books. He gives 6 books to his friend. How many books does Jack have left?
____

4. Sam has 7 T-shirts. 3 are red and the rest are yellow. How many yellow T-shirts does Sam have? ____________________

Circle the letter next to the **true** statement for each question.

5. An apple is a type of fruit. All fruits contain seeds.

If the above statements are true, which one of the following statements must also be true?
A All apples are green.
B Apples contain seeds.
C Horses eat apples.

6. Jon always wears brown shoes on Tuesdays. It is Tuesday today.

If the above statements are true, which one of the following statements must also be true?
A Jon likes shoes.
B Jon's shoes have shoelaces.
C Jon is wearing brown shoes today.

Read the following questions. Work out the answers. Write your answers on the lines.

7. How many days in a week? ____________________
8. How many months in a year? ____________________
9. Which day comes after Monday? ____________________
10. Which month comes after February? ____________________
11. What is the day before Sunday? ____________________
12. Which day comes before Saturday? ____________________

Score:		Time taken:		Target met?	

Target time: **15 minutes**

Read the following information. Work out the answers. Write your answers on the lines.

1. I have a bowl of 8 plums.
   If I share them equally with my sister, how many plums will we each have?
   ____
2. It is 5 o'clock now. What time will it be in 2 hours? ________________
3. The postman is delivering letters.
   He goes to Lily's house first then to Daisy's house.
   Next he goes to Holly's house. He goes to Ben's house last.
   Whose house does he go to second? ________________
4. My mother is making phone calls.
   She calls my gran first.
   Next she calls my uncle and then she calls my aunt.
   Lastly she calls my gran again.
   Who does my mother call third? ________________
5. Lizzie has 5 cats.
   2 have pink collars, 1 has a blue collar and the rest have white collars.
   How many blue and pink collars are there altogether? ________________
6. Gita is decorating some cupcakes.
   6 have sprinkles on top, 3 have white icing and 3 have pink icing.
   The ones with the sprinkles on have yellow icing.
   How many cupcakes have yellow icing? ________________

Fill in the blanks.

7. Wednesday Thursday ________________ Saturday
8. Sunday Monday Tuesday ________________ Thursday
9. spring summer ________________ winter
10. Monday Tuesday Wednesday ________________ Friday
11. January February March ________________ May
12. March April May June ________________

Score:		Time taken:		Target met?	

Section 2 Test 1

Target time: **15 minutes**

Read the following information. Work out the answers. Write your answers on the lines.

1. Zoe is eating a packet of sweets. Half of them have pink wrappers, 4 have yellow wrappers and 2 have green wrappers. There are 12 sweets altogether.
   How many have pink wrappers? ________________

2. Jake's pet tabby cat has 5 kittens. 3 are black, 1 is white and the other is a tabby.
   How many tabby cats are there altogether? ________________

3. Zak and his friends are eating crisps. Alan and Mick have salt and vinegar, Zak has cheese and onion, and Stephen and Jo have sweet chilli.
   How many children are there altogether? ________________

Circle the letter next to the **true** statement for each question.

4. Rishi only eats strawberry ice cream. Strawberry ice cream is pink.

   If the above statements are true, which one of the following statements must also be true?
   A Rishi only eats pink ice cream. **B** Ice cream tastes nice. **C** Sally wants some ice cream.

5. A car has an engine. Engines need fuel to run.

   If the above statements are true, which one of the following statements must also be true?
   A Cars need fuel to run. **B** Petrol is a type of fuel. **C** Garages sell petrol.

6. A hen is a type of bird. All birds lay eggs.

   If the above statements are true, which one of the following statements must also be true?
   A Eggs have a yolk inside. **B** It is hard to break an egg. **C** Hens lay eggs.

Read the following questions. Work out the answers. Write your answers on the lines.

7. How many days are there in 2 weeks? ________________
8. How many months are there in 2 years? ________________
9. Amy is 5 now. How old will she be on her next birthday? ________________
10. Kamil is 6 now. How old will he be on his next birthday? ________________
11. What is the date on the day before 23 March? ________________
12. What date is the day after 28 December? ________________

Score:		**Time taken:**		**Target met?**	

Target time: **12 minutes**

Underline the word in brackets that is **closest** in meaning to the word in capitals.

Example HUGE (mouse, large, elephant, small)

1. SAD (mat, house, room, unhappy)
2. TIRED (old, late, sleepy, nap)
3. CHOOSE (root, lock, table, pick)
4. GOOD (land, carpet, sheet, fine)

Choose the word in brackets that will complete the sentence in the best way. Underline the answer.

Example **Cat** is to **kitten** as **dog** is to (paw, puppy, animal).

5. **Kind** is to **nice** as **mean** is to (tell, sort, nasty).
6. **Cup** is to **drink** as **plate** is to (eat, round, water).
7. **Lie** is to **bed** as **sit** is to (shelf, chair, window).
8. **Dog** is to **growl** as **lion** is to (squeak, giggle, roar).

Underline the word in brackets that is **opposite** in meaning to the word in capitals.

Example SMALL (mouse, large, elephant, small)

9. DARK (night, black, door, light)
10. COLD (drink, winter, sunny, hot)
11. STOP (red, car, go, run)

Read the following information. Work out the answer. Write your answer on the line.

12. There are 28 children in Sam's class. 16 of them are girls.
    How many are boys? ________________

Score:		**Time taken:**		**Target met?**	

Section 2 Test 3

Target time: **12 minutes**

1–4. For each of the words below, choose the correct group. Write its letter on the line.

C = colour **F** = flower

blue ____________ lily ____________

daisy ____________ green ____________

tulip ____________ daffodil ____________

brown ____________ white ____________

In each group, three words go together and one is the odd one out. Underline the word that does **not** go with the other three.

Example one two <u>out</u> six

5. three star one six

6. strawberry carrot banana cherry

7. kind mean friendly nice

8. sofa chair table path

Choose the most sensible word to complete each sentence. Underline the word.

Example A **cat** always has (mice, hair, <u>paws</u>).

9. A **fish** always has (fins, stripes, a net).

10. A **plane** always has (passengers, wings, a driver).

11. A **chicken** always has a (chick, nest, beak).

Read the following information. Work out the answer. Write your answer on the line.

12. Julie and her friends, Alice and Amelia, each buy an ice cream. Amelia has strawberry and chocolate ice cream with a flake, Alice has vanilla ice cream with two flakes and Julie has mint ice cream with no flakes. How many children have flakes in their ice creams?

____

Score:		**Time taken:**		**Target met?**	

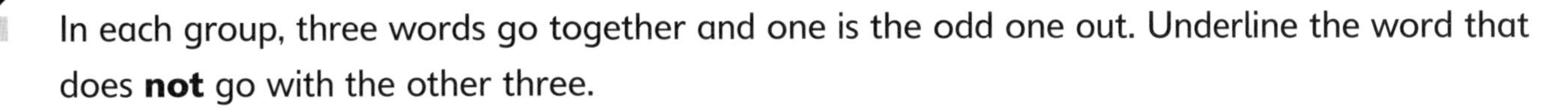
Target time: **12 minutes**

In each group, three words go together and one is the odd one out. Underline the word that does **not** go with the other three.

Example one two <u>out</u> six

1. flower building bush tree
2. dance sleep nap rest
3. magazine book television newspaper
4. dinner lunch breakfast yesterday

Choose the word in brackets that will complete the sentence in the best way. Underline the answer.

Example **Cat** is to **kitten** as **dog** is to (paw, <u>puppy</u>, animal).

5. **Feet** are to **socks** as **hands** are to (coat, trousers, gloves).
6. **Drum** is to **hit** as **whistle** is to (throw, blow, happy).
7. **Light** is to **dark** as **high** is to (low, under, away).
8. **Cat** is to **furry** as **hedgehog** is to (night, cute, prickly).

Underline the two words, **one** from each group, that mean almost the **same**.

Example (hot, <u>cool</u>, heat) (sky, day, <u>cold</u>)

9. (funny, laugh, joke) (giggle, poke, clown)
10. (top, fight, bad) (evil, hill, grass)
11. (smile, coat, wear) (grin, clap, shoes)

Circle the letter next to the **true** statement.

12. A snowdrop is a type of flower. All flowers have petals.

If the above statements are true, which one of the following statements must also be true?

A Snowdrops grow from bulbs.
B Snowdrops have petals.
C All white flowers grow in winter.

Score:		**Time taken:**		**Target met?**	

Section 2 Test 5

Target time: **12 minutes**

Remove **one** letter from each word to make a new, correctly spelt word. Write the new word on the line.

Example trip ___rip___ (remove the t)

1. cup ____________
2. gown ____________
3. seen ____________
4. skunk ____________

In each of the sentences below, the word in capitals has three letters missing. Those three letters spell a word. Write the three-letter word in the gap.

Example She left the door O _P_ _E_ _N_. (OPEN)

5. We saw cows, chickens and horses at the ___ ___ ___ M.
6. Do you K ___ ___ ___ my name?
7. I hope that the rain will go A ___ ___ ___ later.
8. It is Sunday TO ___ ___ ___.

Rearrange the word in capitals. Use the letters to make another word that goes with the first two. Write the new word on the line.

Example arm finger GEL ___LEG___

9. sleep rest PAN ____________
10. pan container TOP ____________
11. eye nose ARE ____________

Read the following information. Work out the answer. Write your answer on the line.

12. Ellie is in the supermarket queue. There are two people in front of her and three behind her. What position is Ellie in the queue? ________________

Score:		**Time taken:**		**Target met?**	

Verbal Reasoning Rapid Tests 1 Answers

Notes for parents, tutors, teachers and other adult helpers

- **Verbal Reasoning Rapid Tests 1** is designed for six- and seven-year-olds, but may also be suitable for some older children.
- Remove this pull-out section before giving the book to the child.
- Before the child begins work on the first test, read together the instructions on page 2, headed **What to do**. As you do so, look together at **Section 1 Test 1** and point out to the child the different elements.
- As each question type is introduced for the first time within a particular test, an example is given. Where question types recur throughout the book, the same example is provided. This is deliberate: the example will act as a useful reminder, but children will not need to work through it repeatedly from scratch.
- Make sure that the child understands how to answer the questions and that he or she has a pencil, an eraser and a sheet of rough paper. You should also ensure that the child is able to see a clock or a watch.
- Be sure that the child knows to tell you clearly when he or she has finished the test.
- When the child is ready, say 'Start the test now' and make a note of the start time.
- When the child has finished, work out how long he or she took to complete the test. Then fill in the **Time taken** box, which appears at the end of the test.
- Mark the child's work using this pull-out section, giving one mark for each correct answer unless instructed otherwise. There are a total of 12 marks available for each test. Then complete the **Score** box at the end of the test.
- The table below shows you how to mark the **Target met?** box and the **Action** notes help you to plan the next step. However, these are suggestions only. Please use your own judgement as you decide how best to proceed.

Score	Time taken*	Target met?	Action
1–6	Any	Not yet	Provide help and support as needed.
7–9	Any	Not yet	Encourage the child to keep practising using the tests in this book. The child may need to repeat some tests. If so, wait a few weeks, or the child may simply remember the correct answers. Provide help and support as needed.
10–12	Over target – child took too long	Not yet	
10–12	On target – child took suggested time or less	Yes	Encourage the child to keep practising using further tests in this book, and to move on to the next book when you think this is appropriate.

* The time taken for the tests varies depending on the types of questions included.

- After finishing each test, the child should fill in the **Progress chart** on page 40.
- Whatever the test score, always encourage the child to have another go at the questions that he or she got wrong – without looking at the solutions. If the child's answers are still incorrect, work through these questions together. Demonstrate the correct method if necessary.
- If the child struggles with particular question types, help him or her to develop the strategies needed.

Answers

Section 1 Test 1 (page 4)

1. quick, fast
2. noisy, loud
3. cold, chilly
4. hippopotamus
5. bike
6. woman
7. big, small
8. day, night
9. in, out
10. truck
11. circle
12. up

Section 1 Test 2 (page 5)

1–3. *[score half a point for each correct answer]*
deer = A, beetle = I, rabbit = A, tiger = A, bee = I, fly = I

4. sun (the others are all animals)
5. door (the rest are colours)
6. monkey (the others are all birds)
7. high, low
8. top, bottom
9. open, shut
10. are old (How old are you?)
11. Is what (What is your name?)
12. live you (Where do you live?)

Section 1 Test 3 (page 6)

1. shut, close
2. angry, cross
3. sick, ill
4. read
5. cry
6. sunny

7–9. *[score half a point for each correct answer]*
apple = F, orange = F, carrot = V, parsnip = V, potato = V, cabbage = V

10. library (the others are to do with the beach)
11. tail (the rest are to do with feet)
12. large (the other words all mean small)

Section 1 Test 4 (page 7)

1. b (bin)
2. h (hip)
3. e (egg)
4. KEY (MONKEY)
5. LAY (PLAY)
6. HOW (SHOW)
7. cap
8. ant
9. pan
10. h (wish and hope)
11. t (boot and tent)
12. l (real and lick)

Section 1 Test 5 (page 8)

1. ILL (BILL)
2. MAT (MATCH)
3. OWN (DOWN)
4. ripple rip
5. thrill ill
6. dear ear
7. ear, are
8. yaw, way
9. how, who
10. roundabout
11. goldfish
12. milkshake

Section 1 Test 6 (page 9)

1. TOP [TIP] NIP
2. PAT [POT] POP
3. SIT [SAT] SAG
4. TOP (STOP)
5. DAY (BIRTHDAY)
6. ALL (FOOTBALL)
7. pancake
8. butterfly
9. classroom
10. try
11. the
12. mat

Section 1 Test 7 (page 10)

1. 11 (+1)
2. 8 (+1)
3. 18 (+1)
4. D (5 + 7 = 12)
5. A (8 + 9 = 17)
6. C (11 + 5 = 16)
7. 15 (a + b)
8. 5 (a − b)
9. 10 (a + b)
10. 2
11. 3
12. 1

Section 1 Test 8 (page 11)

1. 15 (a + b)
2. 16 (a + b)
3. 5 (a − b)
4. 10
5. 9
6. 0
7. 32 (+1)
8. 42 (−1)
9. 13 (+2)
10. D (3 + 6 = 9)
11. A (7 + 4 = 11)
12. A (15 − 6 = 9)

Section 1 Test 9 (page 12)

1. Q (+1)
2. O (−1)
3. G (repeating pattern)
4. D (−1)
5. K (+3)
6. D (+2)
7. hope
8. pan
9. mate
10. 465
11. 413
12. ONE

Section 1 Test 10 (page 13)

1. QPU (+1)
2. FOE (+1)
3. CPZ (+1)
4. 135
5. 174
6. USE
7. sat
8. its
9. bun
10. S (repeating pattern)
11. W (repeating pattern)
12. Y (+1)

Section 1 Test 11 (page 14)

1. second (accept 'middle')
2. third (accept 'last')
3. 5
4. 4
5. B
6. C
7. 7
8. 12
9. Tuesday
10. March
11. Saturday
12. Friday

Section 1 Test 12 (page 15)

1. 4
2. 7 o'clock (accept variations)
3. Daisy's house
4. my aunt
5. 3
6. 6
7. Friday
8. Wednesday
9. autumn
10. Thursday
11. April
12. July

Answers

Section 2 Test 1 (page 16)

1. 6
2. 2 (mother cat and 1 kitten)
3. 5
4. A
5. A
6. C
7. 14
8. 24
9. 6
10. 7
11. 22 March
12. 29 December

Section 2 Test 2 (page 17)

1. unhappy
2. sleepy
3. pick
4. fine
5. nasty
6. eat
7. chair
8. roar
9. light
10. hot
11. go
12. 12

Section 2 Test 3 (page 18)

1–4. *[score half a point for each correct answer]*
blue = C, daisy = F, tulip = F, brown = C,
lily = F, green = C, daffodil = F, white = C

5. star (the others are numbers)
6. carrot (the others are fruits)
7. mean (the others describe a nice person)
8. path (the rest are furniture)
9. fins
10. wings
11. beak
12. 2

Section 2 Test 4 (page 19)

1. building (the others are all plants)
2. dance (the others describe resting)
3. television (you read all the others)
4. yesterday (the rest are meals)
5. gloves
6. blow
7. low
8. prickly
9. laugh, giggle
10. bad, evil
11. smile, grin
12. B

Section 2 Test 5 (page 20)

1. up (remove c)
2. own (remove g)
3. see (remove n)
4. sunk (remove k)
5. FAR (FARM)
6. NOW (KNOW)
7. WAY (AWAY)
8. DAY (TODAY)
9. NAP
10. POT
11. EAR
12. third

Section 2 Test 6 (page 21)

1. G I N S
2. G
3. A P R T Y
4. P
5. MOW [COW] COT
6. LIE [TIE] TIN
7. LAG [BAG] BIG
8. BIN [BAN] CAN
9. seaside
10. sunlight
11. hosepipe
12. 16

Section 2 Test 7 (page 22)

1. what hat
2. asked ask
3. lone one
4. fragile rag
5. n (bean and nice)
6. p (trip and push)
7. k (pick and kite)
8. starfish
9. sandpit
10. flowerpot
11. postbox
12. 3

Section 2 Test 8 (page 23)

1. 12 (+2)
2. 32 (+2)
3. 50 (+10)
4. 50 (−10)
5. B ($18 - 9 = 9$)
6. D ($9 + 11 = 20$)
7. C ($15 - 3 = 12$)
8. D ($7 + 6 = 13$)
9. 18 ($a + b$)
10. 11 ($a + b$)
11. 10 ($a + b$)
12. Lin

Section 2 Test 9 (page 24)

1. 1
2. 1
3. 8
4. 10
5. 45 (+1)
6. 1 (repeating pattern)
7. 20 (counting forwards in 5s)
8. 14 (−1)
9. B ($20 - 13 = 7$)
10. D ($15 - 8 = 7$)
11. C ($10 - 8 = 2$)
12. 14

Section 2 Test 10 (page 25)

1. 5 ($a \times b$)
2. 13 ($a + b$)
3. 4 ($a \div b$)
4. 11 ($a + b$)
5. 1
6. 3
7. 7
8. C ($3 + 18 = 21$)
9. A ($22 - 12 = 10$)
10. B ($13 + 14 = 27$)
11. C ($18 - 7 + 11$)
12. C

Section 2 Test 11 (page 26)

1. lot
2. pan
3. hop
4. loot
5. 251
6. 283
7. 281
8. PEA
9. K (+1)
10. I (+1)
11. M (repeating pattern)
12. 30 minutes or half an hour

Section 2 Test 12 (page 27)

1. tool
2. soup
3. top
4. sir
5. LHRR (−1)
6. QNV (−1)
7. MNV (−1)
8. TRD (−1)
9. H (−1)
10. N (+3)
11. Z (+1)
12. 20

Answers

Section 3 Test 1 (page 28)

1–4. *[score half a point for each correct answer]* rectangle = A, bowl = B, cup = B, fork = B, knife = B, kite = A, circle = A, hexagon = A
5. 15 (+3)
6. 5 (repeating pattern)
7. *** (alternate symbols increase by one each time)
8. 27 (−1)
9. eyeball
10. skateboard
11. handstand
12. second (accept 'middle')

Section 3 Test 2 (page 29)

1. 8 ($a - b$)
2. 19 ($a - b$)
3. 15 ($a - b$)
4. 18 ($a \times b$)
5. RUN
6. WET
7. FUN
8. ODD
9. TIE (TIED)
10. ROW (GROW)
11. NOW (SNOW)
12. A

Section 3 Test 3 (page 30)

1. led (remove s)
2. rink (remove b)
3. rip (remove g)
4. sigh (remove t)
5. 1
6. 8
7. 10
8. 2
9. 863
10. 427
11. TEN
12. third

Section 3 Test 4 (page 31)

1. rub
2. kit
3. rip
4. jug
5. R (−1)
6. N (+3)
7. E (−3)
8. Y (+2)
9. D ($30 - 16 = 14$)
10. D ($12 + 23 = 35$)
11. B ($10 + 11 = 21$)
12. 70p

Section 3 Test 5 (page 32)

1. flowers likes (My mum likes flowers.)
2. in swim (Fish swim in the sea.)
3. roared lion (The lion roared loudly.)
4. bananas eat (Monkeys eat bananas.)
5. l (deal and like)
6. e (knee and elf)
7. t (root and tile)
8. n (lion and next)
9. A (−1)
10. R (+1)
11. Q (−1)
12. the man

Section 3 Test 6 (page 33)

1. D ($3 \times 6 = 18$)
2. C ($20 \div 10 = 2$)
3. D ($2 \times 6 = 12$)
4. B ($25 \div 5 = 5$)
5. BNS (−1)
6. CNS (−1)
7. KHD (−1)
8. taste, flavour
9. rock, stone
10. boat, ship
11. bite, nip
12. 4

Section 3 Test 7 (page 34)

1. stepmother
2. pathway
3. toothbrush
4. downstairs
5. e (rose and eat)
6. n (town and nine)
7. g (big and good)
8. r (door and room)
9. great eat
10. grinned inn
11. dripped rip
12. 3.45 p.m. or 15:45 or quarter to four

Section 3 Test 8 (page 35)

1. 20 (a − b)
2. 50 (a + b)
3. 15 (a × b)
4. 12 (a − b)
5. good, bad
6. old, young
7. black, white
8. happy, sad
9. WIN [WIG] JIG
10. LOW [LOG] DOG
11. LIE [TIE] TIN
12. B

Section 3 Test 9 (page 36)

1. day
2. slim
3. lop
4. gall
5. cheetah
6. fairy
7. cup
8. run
9. down
10. yellow
11. toy
12. 3

Section 3 Test 10 (page 37)

1. S (−3)
2. W (+2)
3. F (−3)
4. G (+3)
5. night (the others are to do with the weather)
6. short (the others describe how something feels)
7. wet (the others all describe the cold)
8. bag (the others are all something you can write with)
9. K (+2)
10. V (+2)
11. U (+3)
12. £6 or £6.00

Section 3 Test 11 (page 38)

1. messy
2. banana
3. dog
4. pond
5. 95 (−1)
6. ☹ (repeating pattern)
7. £ (repeating pattern)
8. 40 (counting backwards in 5s)
9. wow
10. dog
11. when
12. 6

Section 3 Test 12 (page 39)

1. 3
2. 2
3. 5
4. 2
5. 213
6. 512
7. PAL
8. push, pull
9. boy, girl
10. easy, hard
11. on, off
12. B

This book of answers is a pull-out section from
Verbal Reasoning Rapid Tests 1

Published by ***Schofield & Sims Ltd****,*
7 Mariner Court, Wakefield, West Yorkshire WF4 3FL, UK
Telephone 01484 607080
www.schofieldandsims.co.uk

First published in 2014

Second impression 2019

Author: ***Siân Goodspeed***

British Library Cataloguing in Publication Data
A catalogue record for this book is available from the British Library.

Commissioned by ***Carolyn Richardson Publishing Services*** *(www.publiserve.co.uk)*

Design by ***Oxford Designers & Illustrators***
Printed in the UK by ***Page Bros (Norwich) Ltd***

ISBN 978 07217 1450 9

Target time: **12 minutes**

Answer the questions below. Use the alphabet to help you. Write your answers on the lines.

A B C D E F G H I J K L M N O P Q R S T U V W X Y Z

1–2. Put the letters in the word **SING** into alphabetical order. ____________

Which letter is now the **first** letter? ____________

3–4. Put the letters in the word **PARTY** into alphabetical order. ____________

Which letter is now the **second** letter? ____________

Change the first word into the last word. Only change **one** letter at a time. You must make a new word in the middle. Write the new word on the line.

Example MAN [PAN] PIN

5. MOW [____________] COT

6. LIE [____________] TIN

7. LAG [____________] BIG

8. BIN [____________] CAN

Underline the two words, **one** from each group, that together make one new word. The word from the first group comes first.

Example (foot, head, face) (shoe, ball, mask) (football)

9. (stream, sea, ocean) (side, behind, counter)

10. (planet, sun, wind) (light, heavy, weigh)

11. (hose, rope, rubber) (tunnel, pipe, garden)

Read the following information. Work out the answer. Write your answer on the line.

12. Daniel gives half of his toy car collection to his friend, Ola. He gives 8 to Ola.
How many cars did Daniel have to begin with? ____________

Score:		Time taken:		Target met?	

Section 2 Test 7

Target time: **12 minutes**

Find the **three-letter word** hidden in each longer word. You will not need to change the letter order. Underline the word and write it on the line.

Example lathe ___the___

1. what ________
2. asked ________
3. lone ________
4. fragile ________

Find the missing letter that completes **both** words. Write the letter on the line. Choose your answer from these letters:

p t k n

Example tap (_e_) at (tape and eat)

5. bea (__) ice
6. tri (__) ush
7. pic (__) ite

Underline the two words, **one** from each group, that together make one new word. The word from the first group comes first.

Example (foot, head, face) (shoe, ball, mask) (football)

8. (star, sky, cloud) (sea, fish, fire)
9. (dust, soil, sand) (pit, mine, dig)
10. (flower, leaf, plants) (hold, pot, grow)
11. (card, stamp, post) (fire, box, ladder)

Read the following information. Work out the answer. Write your answer on the line.

12. There are 6 puppies in a litter. 2 are brown, 1 is black and the rest are cream.
How many cream puppies are there? ________________

Score:		Time taken:		Target met?	

Target time: 12 minutes

Find the next number in the sequence. Write it on the line.

Example 14 15 16 17 18 19 (+1 each time)

1. 2 4 6 8 10 ______
2. 24 26 28 30 ______
3. 10 20 30 40 ______
4. 100 90 80 70 60 ______

Use the information given to answer the sum. Write your answer as a **letter**.

Example A = 1 B = 2 C = 3 D = 5 A + B = C (1 + 2 = 3)

5. A = 18 B = 9 C = 16 D = 13 **A – B =** ______
6. A = 9 B = 10 C = 11 D = 20 **A + C =** ______
7. A = 13 B = 3 C = 12 D = 15 **D – B =** ______
8. A = 12 B = 6 C = 7 D = 13 **C + B =** ______

Work out the missing number. Write it on the line.

Example 3 [5] 2 4 [6] 2 5 [8] 3
(a + b = ?, where a is the number on the left and b is the number on the right)

9. 2 [13] 11 4 [16] 12 11 [______] 7
10. 11 [12] 1 12 [15] 3 7 [______] 4
11. 10 [12] 2 9 [10] 1 8 [______] 2

Read the following information. Work out the answer. Write your answer on the line.

12. Three children are in a sack race. Lin finishes ahead of Tommy and Ivan finishes last. Who is first? ______________

Score:		**Time taken:**		**Target met?**	

Section 2 Test 9

Target time: **12 minutes**

Find the missing number in each equation. Write it on the line.

Example 1 + 3 = 2 + __2__ (1 + 3 = 4 and so does 2 + 2)

1. 8 − 4 = 5 − ______
2. 4 + 7 = 10 + ______
3. 18 − 2 = 8 + ______
4. 11 + 19 = 20 + ______

Find the next number in the sequence. Write it on the line.

Example 14 15 16 17 18 __19__ (+1 each time)

5. 41 42 43 44 ______
6. 1 0 1 0 ______
7. 5 10 15 ______ 25
8. 19 18 17 16 15 ______

Use the information given to answer the sum. Write your answer as a **letter**.

Example A = 1 B = 2 C = 3 D = 5 **A + B =** __C__ (1 + 2 = 3)

9. A = 20 B = 7 C = 13 D = 8 **A − C =** ______
10. A = 15 B = 14 C = 8 D = 7 **A − C =** ______
11. A = 11 B = 8 C = 2 D = 10 **D − B =** ______

Read the following information. Work out the answer. Write your answer on the line.

12. Jamie is 2 years older than Mikail. Mikail is 12 years old. How old is Jamie?

______

Score:		**Time taken:**		**Target met?**	

Target time: **12 minutes**

Work out the missing number. Write it on the line.

Example 3 [5] 2 4 [6] 2 5 [8] 3
(a + b = ?, where a is the number on the left and b is the number on the right)

1. 2 [4] 2 3 [6] 2 5 [_____] 1
2. 7 [15] 8 6 [14] 8 3 [_____] 10
3. 4 [2] 2 12 [6] 2 8 [_____] 2
4. 8 [12] 4 9 [13] 4 7 [_____] 4

Find the missing number in each equation. Write it on the line.

Example 1 + 3 = 2 + 2 (1 + 3 = 4 and so does 2 + 2)

5. 12 − 1 = 10 + _____
6. 14 − 8 = 9 − _____
7. 16 − 8 = 1 + _____

Use the information given to answer the sum. Write your answer as a **letter**.

Example A = 1 B = 2 C = 3 D = 5 **A + B =** C (1 + 2 = 3)

8. A = 18 B = 3 C = 21 D = 9 **B + A =** _____
9. A = 10 B = 12 C = 18 D = 22 **D − B =** _____
10. A = 13 B = 27 C = 17 D = 14 **A + D =** _____
11. A = 13 B = 18 C = 11 D = 7 **B − D =** _____

Circle the letter next to the **true** statement.

12. All fish swim in water. Plaice are a type of fish.

If the above statements are true, which one of the following statements must also be true?

A Chips go with fish.
B Fish have scales.
C Plaice swim in water.

Score:		**Time taken:**		**Target met?**	

Section 2 Test 11

Target time: **15 minutes**

Make a new word. Change the third pair of words in the same way as the other pairs. Write the new word on the line.

Example (mat, at) (fit, it) (son, __on__) (take away the first letter of the first word)

1. (row, rot) (how, hot) (low, __________)
2. (men, man) (ten, tan) (pen, __________)
3. (shut, hut) (sham, ham) (shop, __________)
4. (loop, pool) (room, moor) (tool, __________)

Match the number codes to the words. Use this to help you work out the answers to the questions. Write your answers on the lines.

ANT APE NAP 825 831 382

5. What is the code for **PET**? __________
6. What is the code for **PAN**? __________
7. What is the code for **PAT**? __________
8. What does the code **258** mean? __________

Find the next letter in the sequence. Use the alphabet to help you. Write the letter on the line.

A B C D E F G H I J K L M N O P Q R S T U V W X Y Z

Example A B C D E __F__ (+1 each time)

9. F G H I J ____
10. D E F G H ____
11. L M L M L ____

Read the following information. Work out the answer. Write your answer on the line.

12. Ned starts his homework at 5 p.m. He finishes it at 5.30 p.m.
How long does it take Ned to do his homework? _______________

Score:		**Time taken:**		**Target met?**	

Target time: **15 minutes**

The word in square brackets has been made by some of the letters from the two outside words. Make a new word in the middle of the second group of words in the same way. Write the new word on the line.

Example (toe [tap] rap) (low [lit] sit)

1. (do [door] ore) (to [____________] old)
2. (one [onto] too) (so [____________] up)
3. (ted [ten] nest) (toll [____________] pen)
4. (out [our] ram) (sit [____________] rid)

Find the code. Use the alphabet to help you. Write the code on the line.

A B C D E F G H I J K L M N O P Q R S T U V W X Y Z

Example If the code for **TOP** is **UPQ**, what is the code for **TIP**? UJQ (+1 each time)

5. If the code for **YOU** is **XNT**, what is the code for **MISS**? ____________
6. If the code for **TOO** is **SNN**, what is the code for **ROW**? ____________
7. If the code for **ONE** is **NMD**, what is the code for **NOW**? ____________
8. If the code for **LOT** is **KNS**, what is the code for **USE**? ____________

Find the letter that completes each sentence. Use the alphabet to help you. Write the letter on the line.

A B C D E F G H I J K L M N O P Q R S T U V W X Y Z

Example **A** is to **B** as **D** is to E. (+1 each time)

9. **G** is to **F** as **I** is to ____.
10. **U** is to **X** as **K** is to ____.
11. **D** is to **E** as **Y** is to ____.

Read the following information. Work out the answer. Write your answer on the line.

12. There are 40 sweets in a pack. Mirjana shares them equally with her friend Stefan. How many sweets does each child have? ____________

Score:		**Time taken:**		**Target met?**	

Target time: **12 minutes**

1–4. Look at these groups. For each of the words below, choose the correct group. Write its letter on the line.

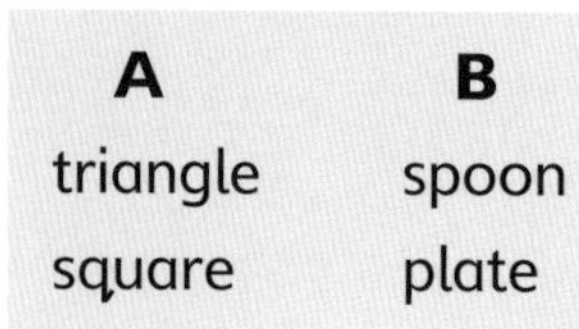

A	B
triangle	spoon
square	plate

rectangle ____________ knife ____________

bowl ____________ kite ____________

cup ____________ circle ____________

fork ____________ hexagon ____________

Find the next number or symbol in the sequence. Write it on the line.

Example 14 15 16 17 18 __19__ (+1 each time)

5. 3 6 9 12 ______ 18

6. 2 5 2 5 2 ______ 2

7. ! * !! ** !!! ______

8. 30 29 28 ______ 26

Underline the two words, **one** from each group, that together make one new word. The word from the first group comes first.

Example (foot, head, face) (shoe, ball, mask) (football)

9. (lip, cheek, eye) (cricket, basket, ball)

10. (slip, skate, run) (board, jump, ski)

11. (arm, leg, hand) (finger, stand, stretch)

Read the following information. Work out the answer. Write your answer on the line.

12. Samit is in a race with two of his friends. Josh finishes in front of Samit and Niall comes last. Where does Samit finish? ________________

Score:		Time taken:		Target met?	

Target time: **12 minutes**

Work out the missing number. Write it on the line.

Example 3 [5] 2   4 [6] 2   5 [8] 3
(a + b = ?, where a is the number on the left and b is the number on the right)

1. 23 [9] 14   21 [9] 12   23 [______] 15
2. 17 [15] 2   19 [17] 2   21 [______] 2
3. 21 [7] 14   28 [14] 14   30 [______] 15
4. 6 [12] 2   8 [16] 2   9 [______] 2

Rearrange the word in capitals. Use the letters to make a new word. The sentence must make sense. Write the new word on the line.

Example The **NUS** shone brightly. SUN

5. I had to **NRU** fast to win the race. ______
6. The weather was **TWE**. ______
7. James had **NFU** at the fair. ______
8. Three is an **DDO** number. ______

In each of the sentences below, the word in capitals has three letters missing. Those three letters spell a word. Write the three-letter word in the gap.

Example She left the door O P E N .   (OPEN)

9. I _ _ _ D my shoelaces.
10. I hope the flower will G _ _ _ very tall.
11. The S _ _ _ was cold and white.

Circle the letter next to the **true** statement.

12. Lions are a type of big cat. Big cats hunt for food.

If the above statements are true, which one of the following statements must also be true?

- **A** Lions hunt for their food.
- **B** Lions are always hungry.
- **C** Lions like food.

Score:		**Time taken:**		**Target met?**	

Target time: **12 minutes**

Remove **one** letter from each of the words below to make a new, correctly spelt word. Write the new word on the line.

Example trip ___rip___ (remove the t)

1. sled ____________
2. brink ____________
3. grip ____________
4. sight ____________

Find the missing number in each equation. Write it on the line.

Example $1 + 3 = 2 +$ ___2___ ($1 + 3 = 4$ and so does $2 + 2$)

5. $20 - 7 = 14 -$ ______
6. $19 - 3 = 8 +$ ______
7. $24 - 4 = 10 +$ ______
8. $70 - 9 = 59 +$ ______

Match the number codes to the words. Use this to help you work out the answers to the questions. Write your answers on the lines.

BIN NEW BET 368 327 824

9. What is the code for **NIB**? ____________
10. What is the code for **WET**? ____________
11. What does the code **728** mean? ____________

Read the following information. Work out the answer. Write your answer on the line.

12. Luca lives in a block of flats. His flat is on the first floor. His neighbour, Frankie, lives in a flat two floors above him. On which floor does Frankie live? ____________________

Score:		Time taken:		Target met?	

Target time: **12 minutes**

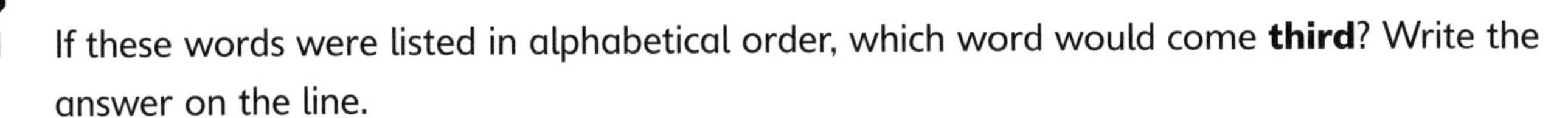

If these words were listed in alphabetical order, which word would come **third**? Write the answer on the line.

Example dog cat vet sit cow ___dog___

1. tin pot sow rub lid ________
2. man kit dip lie bid ________
3. rip wit and bow zoo ________
4. ivy jug wet can pig ________

Find the letter that completes each sentence. Use the alphabet to help you. Write the letter on the line.

A B C D E F G H I J K L M N O P Q R S T U V W X Y Z

Example **A** is to **B** as **D** is to ___E___. (+1 each time)

5. **F** is to **E** as **S** is to _____ .
6. **B** is to **E** as **K** is to _____ .
7. **T** is to **Q** as **H** is to _____ .
8. **E** is to **G** as **W** is to _____ .

Use the information given to answer the sum. Write your answer as a **letter**.

Example A = 1 B = 2 C = 3 D = 5 **A + B =** ___C___ (1 + 2 = 3)

9. A = 34 B = 16 C = 30 D = 14 **C − B =** ______
10. A = 23 B = 12 C = 25 D = 35 **B + A =** ______
11. A = 19 B = 21 C = 11 D = 10 **D + C =** ______

Read the following information. Work out the answer. Write your answer on the line.

12. George paid 35p each for 2 lollies. How much did he pay altogether? ____________

Score:		**Time taken:**		**Target met?**	

Target time: **12 minutes**

Two words in each sentence must change places so that the sentence makes sense. Underline the two words.

Example Where do you to go school? (Where do you go to school?)

1. My mum flowers likes.
2. Fish in swim the sea.
3. The roared lion loudly.
4. Monkeys bananas eat.

Find the missing letter that completes **both** words. Write the letter on the line. Choose your answer from these letters:

l r e k n t

Example tap (e) at (tape and eat)

5. dea (__) ike
6. kne (__) lf
7. roo (__) ile
8. lio (__) ext

Find the next letter in the sequence. Use the alphabet to help you. Write the letter on the line.

A B C D E F G H I J K L M N O P Q R S T U V W X Y Z

Example A B C D E F (+1 each time)

9. F E D C B ____
10. M N O P Q ____
11. V U T S R ____

Read the following information. Work out the answer. Write your answer on the line.

12. A man, a woman and a boy are in a bus queue. The boy gets on to the bus first, then the woman and finally the man. Who gets on the bus last? ____________

Score: | **Time taken:** | **Target met?**

Target time: **12 minutes**

Use the information given to answer the sum. Write your answer as a **letter**.

Example A = 1 B = 2 C = 3 D = 5 **A + B =** C (1 + 2 = 3)

1. A = 4 B = 6 C = 3 D = 18 **C × B =** ______
2. A = 20 B = 10 C = 2 D = 5 **A ÷ B =** ______
3. A = 9 B = 2 C = 6 D = 12 **B × C =** ______
4. A = 25 B = 5 C = 10 D = 4 **A ÷ B =** ______

Find the code. Use the alphabet to help you. Write the code on the line.

A B C D E F G H I J K L M N O P Q R S T U V W X Y Z

Example If the code for **TOP** is **UPQ**, what is the code for **TIP**? UJQ (+1 each time)

5. If the code for **RED** is **QDC**, what is the code for **COT**? ______
6. If the code for **COD** is **BNC**, what is the code for **DOT**? ______
7. If the code for **UP** is **TO**, what is the code for **LIE**? ______

Underline the pair of words that mean almost the **same**.

Example (hot, cool) (freezing, sunny) (cool, cold)

8. (drink, lick) (taste, flavour) (buy, give)
9. (rock, stone) (soft, sky) (tree, beach)
10. (boat, ship) (tea, fish) (stick, stream)
11. (lift, hit) (cry, smack) (bite, nip)

Read the following information. Work out the answer. Write your answer on the line.

12. There are 9 flowers in a vase. 3 are yellow, 2 are red and the rest are blue.
    How many blue flowers are there? ______

Score:		**Time taken:**		**Target met?**	

Section 3 Test 7

Target time: **12 minutes**

Underline the two words, **one** from each group, that together make one new word. The word from the first group comes first.

Example (foot, head, face) (shoe, ball, mask) (football)

1. (step, stair, climb) (friend, mother, house)
2. (track, to, path) (way, go, yes)
3. (tooth, mouth, smile) (hair, brush, white)
4. (look, in, down) (see, over, stairs)

Find the missing letter that completes **both** words. Write the letter on the line. Choose your answers from these letters:

g n t r e

Example tap (e) at (tape and eat)

5. ros (__) at
6. tow (__) ine
7. bi (__) ood
8. doo (__) oom

Find the **three-letter word** hidden in each longer word. You will not need to change the letter order. Underline the word and write it on the line.

Example lathe the

9. great ____________
10. grinned ____________
11. dripped ____________

Read the following information. Work out the answer. Write your answer on the line.

12. Priya leaves school at 3.30 p.m. It takes her 15 minutes to get home.
What time does she arrive home? ____________

Score:		Time taken:		Target met?	

Target time: **12 minutes**

Work out the missing number. Write it on the line.

Example 3 [5] 2   4 [6] 2   5 [8] 3
(a + b = ?, where a is the number on the left and b is the number on the right)

1. 21 [20] 1   23 [20] 3   26 [______] 6
2. 22 [32] 10   17 [30] 13   35 [______] 15
3. 3 [6] 2   4 [20] 5   3 [______] 5
4. 14 [10] 4   15 [6] 9   20 [______] 8

Underline the two words, **one** from each group, that are most **opposite** in meaning.

Example (large, down, in)   (tiny, tree, hat)

5. (kind, good, star)   (bad, great, cross)
6. (old, little, pot)   (fast, sister, young)
7. (bag, black, paint)   (white, snow, toe)
8. (fun, clown, happy)   (cry, sad, book)

Change the first word into the last word. Only change **one** letter at a time. You must make a new word in the middle. Write the new word on the line.

Example MAN [PAN] PIN

9. WIN [______] JIG
10. LOW [______] DOG
11. LIE [______] TIN

Circle the letter next to the **true** statement.

12. Apes like to eat fruit. Monkeys are a type of ape.

If the above statements are true, which one of the following statements must also be true?

A All fruit is healthy.
B Monkeys like to eat fruit.
C Monkeys have tails.

Score:		**Time taken:**		**Target met?**	

Section 3 Test 9

Target time: **12 minutes**

Make a new word. Change the third pair of words in the same way as the other pairs. Write the new word on the line.

Example (mat, at) (fit, it) (son, on) (take away the first letter of the first word)

1. (bug, dug) (bin, din) (bay, __________)
2. (plane, plan) (twine, twin) (slime, __________)
3. (mood, mod) (soon, son) (loop, __________)
4. (old, gold) (ill, gill) (all, __________)

Underline the word that goes best with the three words in brackets.

Example (bonnet, cap, beanie) hat, coat, shoes

5. (tiger, lion, leopard) cheetah, elephant, seal
6. (elf, pixie, gnome) fairy, giant, castle
7. (mug, glass, beaker) plate, cup, tree
8. (jump, skip, hop) sleep, cry, run

Choose the word in brackets that will complete the sentence in the best way. Underline the answer.

Example **Cat** is to **kitten** as **dog** is to (paw, puppy, animal).

9. **Pull** is to **push** as **up** is to (door, out, down).
10. **Strawberry** is to **red** as **lemon** is to (purple, blue, yellow).
11. **Write** is to **pen** as **play** is to (toy, spoon, shoe).

Read the following information. Work out the answer. Write your answer on the line.

12. Lucy has a collection of 6 teddy bears. Half are brown, 2 are black and 1 is pink. How many are brown? __________

Score:		**Time taken:**		**Target met?**	

Target time: **12 minutes**

Find the letter that completes each sentence. Use the alphabet to help you. Write the letter on the line.

A B C D E F G H I J K L M N O P Q R S T U V W X Y Z

Example **A** is to **B** as **D** is to _E_. (+1 each time)

1. **P** is to **M** as **V** is to ____ .
2. **A** is to **C** as **U** is to ____ .
3. **Z** is to **W** as **I** is to ____ .
4. **P** is to **S** as **D** is to ____ .

In each group, three words go together and one is the odd one out. Underline the word that does **not** go with the other three.

Example one two out six

5. rain snow sun night
6. soft silky short smooth
7. cold freezing icy wet
8. pen bag pencil crayon

Find the next letter in the sequence. Use the alphabet to help you. Write the letter on the line.

A B C D E F G H I J K L M N O P Q R S T U V W X Y Z

Example A B C D E _F_ (+1 each time)

9. A C E G I ____
10. L N P R T ____
11. F I L O R ____

Read the following information. Work out the answer. Write your answer on the line.

12. Freddie paid £2 each for some toy cars. He bought 3 cars.
How much did he pay altogether? ____________

Score: | **Time taken:** | **Target met?**

Section 3 Test 11

Target time: **12 minutes**

Choose the word in brackets that will complete the sentence in the best way. Underline the answer.

Example **Cat** is to **kitten** as **dog** is to (paw, puppy, animal).

1. **Clean** is to **dirty** as **tidy** is to (messy, lost, fresh).
2. **Red** is to **cherry** as **yellow** is to (apple, pea, banana).
3. **Roar** is to **lion** as **bark** is to (horse, dog, fish).
4. **Octopus** is to **sea** as **frog** is to (house, hutch, pond).

Find the next number or symbol in the sequence. Write it on the line.

Example 14 15 16 17 18 19 (+1 each time)

5. 99 98 97 96 ______ 94
6. ☺ ☹ ☺ ______ ☺
7. £ $! £ $! ______
8. 60 55 50 45 ______

The word in square brackets has been made by some of the letters from the two outside words. Make a new word in the middle of the second group of words in the same way. Write the new word on the line.

Example (toe [tap] rap) (low [lit] sit)

9. (lap [lad] dim) (won [______] wed)
10. (tow [tea] ear) (dip [______] ogre)
11. (see [star] tar) (we [______] hen)

Read the following information. Work out the answer. Write your answer on the line.

12. Lulu will be 7 on her next birthday. How old is she now? ______

Score:		**Time taken:**		**Target met?**	

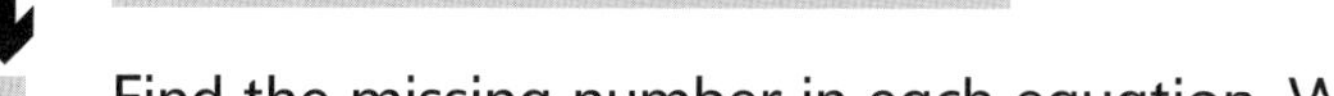

Target time: **12 minutes**

Find the missing number in each equation. Write it on the line.

Example 1 + 3 = 2 + <u>2</u> (1 + 3 = 4 and so does 2 + 2)

1. 20 − 3 = 14 + ______
2. 14 − 7 = 5 + ______
3. 10 × 2 = 15 + ______
4. 50 ÷ 10 = 3 + ______

Match the number codes to the words. Use this to help you work out the answers to the questions. Write your answers on the lines.

PET PAT ALL 732 712 355

5. What is the code for **TEA**? ______
6. What is the code for **LET**? ______
7. What does the code **735** mean? ______

Underline the pair of words that are most **opposite** in meaning.

Example (<u>big, small</u>) (down, round) (elephant, house)

8. (push, pull) (pat, cook) (shut, close)
9. (dress, brother) (boy, girl) (hair, sock)
10. (real, stuck) (easy, hard) (very, maybe)
11. (light, me) (button, letter) (on, off)

Circle the letter next to the **true** statement.

12. A daisy is a type of flower. All flowers have a stem.

If the above statements are true, which one of the following statements must also be true?

A Daisies are pretty.
B Daisies have a stem.
C All daisies are white.

Score:		**Time taken:**		**Target met?**	

Progress chart

Write the score (out of 12) for each test in the box provided on the right of the graph. Then colour in the row next to the box to represent this score.

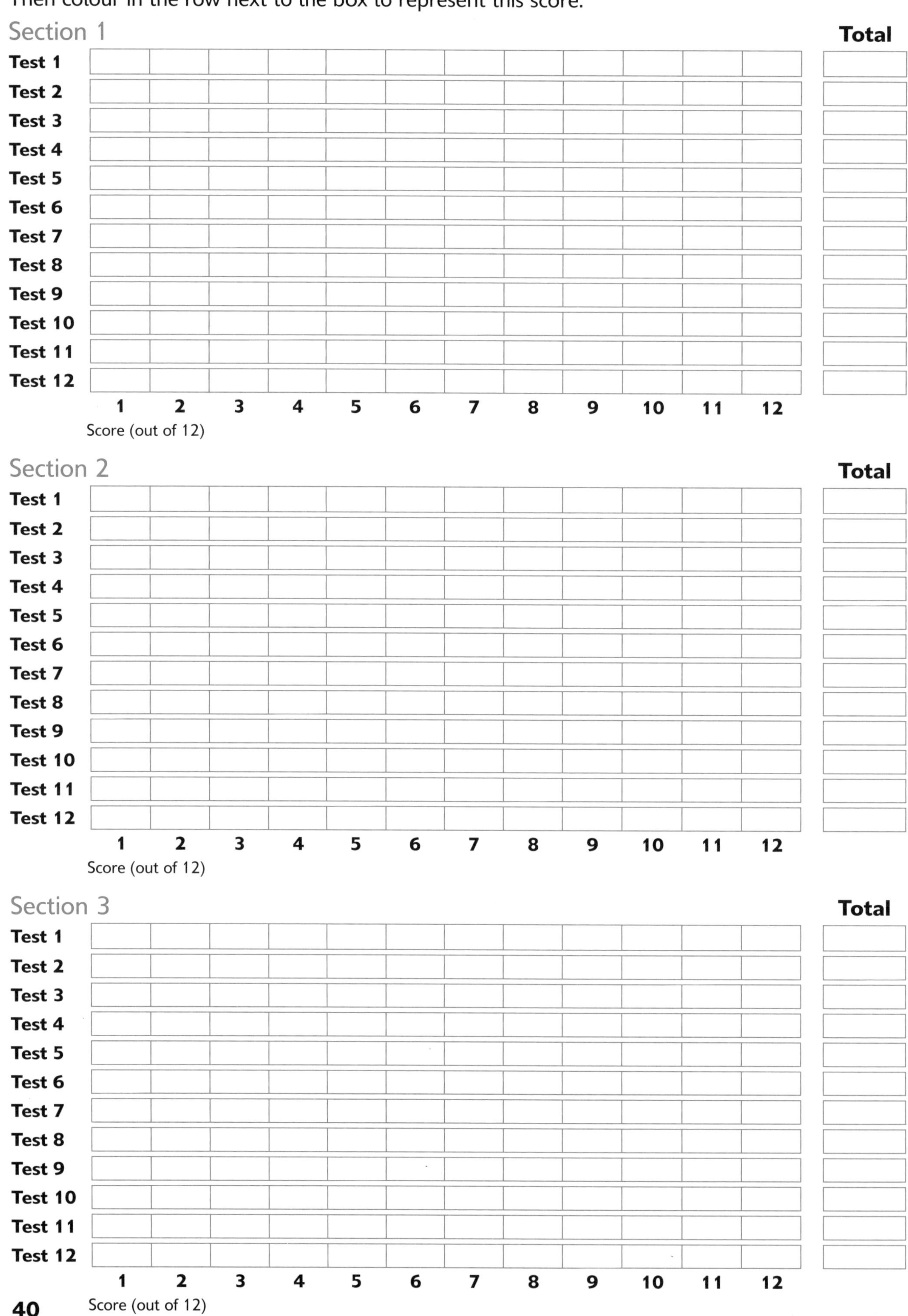